The Usborne Farmyard Tales Songbook

Anthony Marks
Illustrated by Stephen Cartwright
Designed by Amanda Gulliver
Edited by Jenny Tyler

This is Apple Tree Farm.

Mr. and Mrs. Boot live here with their two children, Poppy and Sam. They have a dog called Rusty, a cat called Whiskers, a sheep called Woolly, a pig called Curly and a donkey called Ears. Ted drives the tractor and helps look after all the animals on the farm. Farmer Dray and his carthorse, Dolly, live on the farm next door.

There is a little yellow duck to find on every double page.

Sam and Poppy had a farm

(to the tune of "Old Macdonald had a farm")

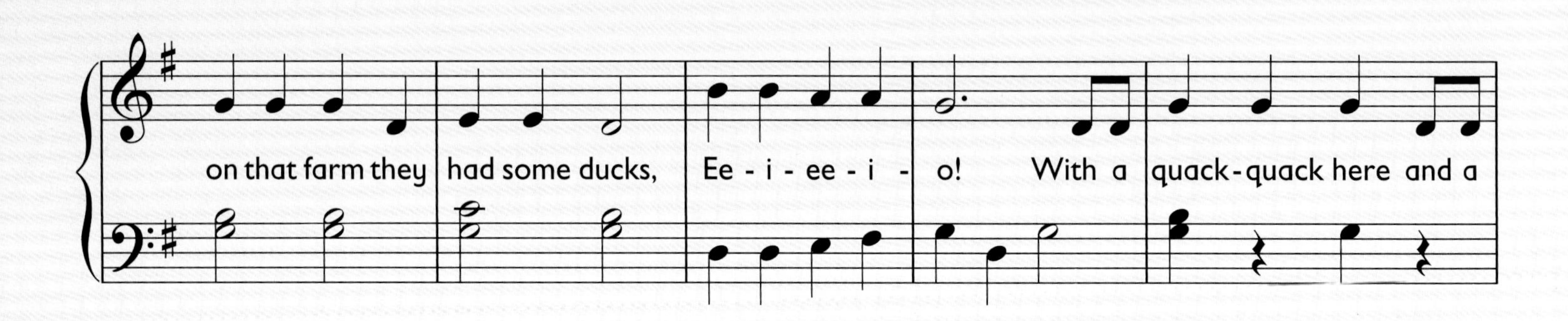

Sam and Poppy had a farm, Ee-i-ee-i-o!
And on that farm they had some ducks, Ee-i-ee-i-o!
With a quack-quack here and a quack-quack there,
Here a quack, there a quack, everywhere a quack-quack!
Sam and Poppy had a farm, Ee-i-ee-i-o!

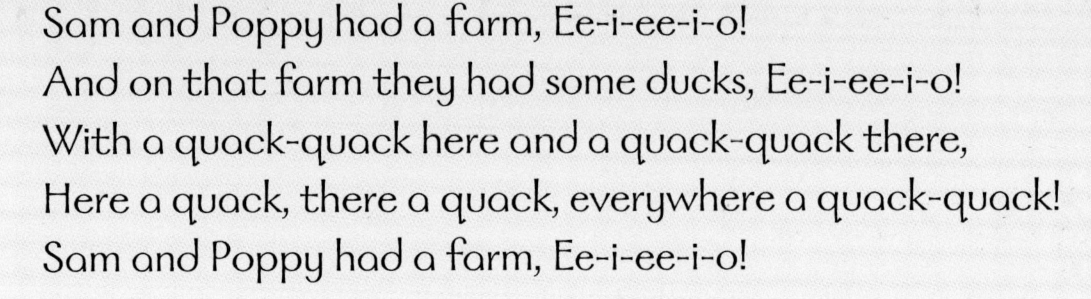

Sam and Poppy had a farm, Ee-i-ee-i-o!
And on that farm they had some pigs, Ee-i-ee-i-o!
With an oink-oink here and an oink-oink there,
Here an oink, there an oink, everywhere an oink-oink!
Sam and Poppy had a farm, Ee-i-ee-i-o!

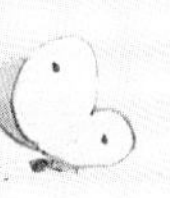

Sam and Poppy had a farm, Ee-i-ee-i-o!
And on that farm they had some sheep, Ee-i-ee-i-o!
With a baa-baa here and a baa-baa there,
Here a baa, there a baa, everywhere a baa-baa!
Sam and Poppy had a farm, Ee-i-ee-i-o!

Sam and Poppy had a farm, Ee-i-ee-i-o!
And on that farm they had some chicks, Ee-i-ee-i-o!
With a chick-chick here and a chick-chick there,
Here a chick, there a chick, everywhere a chick-chick!
Sam and Poppy had a farm, Ee-i-ee-i-o!

Where has our little pig gone?

(to the tune of "Where has my little dog gone?")

Where, oh where has our little pig gone?
Oh where, oh where can he be?
He's not in the cowshed, he's not in the barn,
Oh where, oh where can he be?

Hungry donkey

(to the tune of "London Bridge is falling down")

Ears is going to the show,
To the show, to the show,
Ears is going to the show,
Hungry donkey!

Ears is eating someone's hat!
Someone's hat, someone's hat,
Ears is eating someone's hat,
Hungry donkey!

Ears has won a special prize,
Special prize, special prize,
Ears has won a special prize,
Clever donkey!

Naughty Woolly!

(to the tune of "Baa, baa, black sheep")

Naughty Woolly,
Trotted through the gate,
Look at all the flowers she ate!

Went to the show and she stood in the ring,
And she won a silver cup, the clever thing!

Clever Woolly,
Running down the lane,
Now let's take her home again.

How many eggs?

(to a new tune)

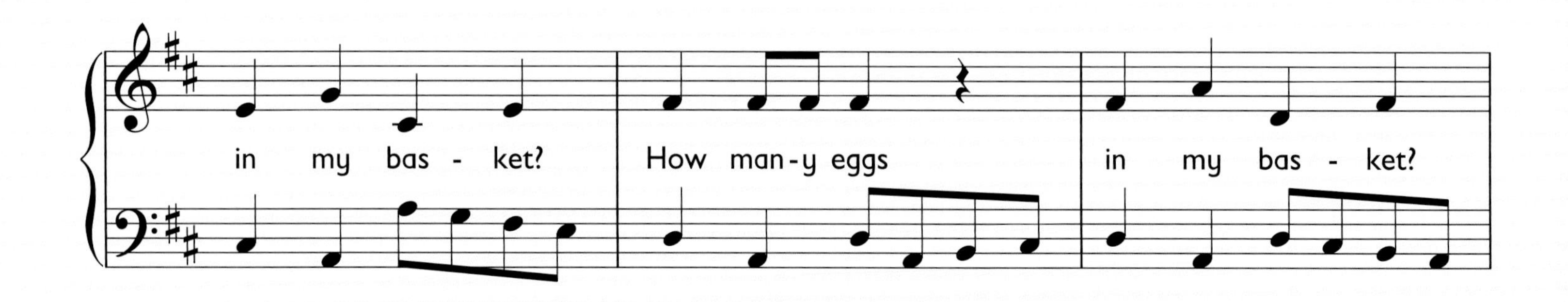

How many eggs in my basket?
How many eggs in my basket?
How many eggs in my basket?
Help me count as I feed the hens.

One, two, three, four,
Five, six, seven, eight, nine, ten!

Sam's little kitten

(to the tune of "Pussycat, pussycat")

Sam's little kitten has gone for a ride,
Off went the truck with her hiding inside!
Now we'll go searching with Ted in the car,
I hope that Fluff hasn't gone very far!

Now we are home at the end of the day,
We haven't found her, has she run away?
Here's Mister Bran, he's got Fluff in his arms,
Now she is safe back at Apple Tree Farm.

Dolly, Dolly

(to the tune of "Horsey, horsey")

Dolly, Dolly, don't you stop!
Just let your feet go clippety-clop,
Your tail goes "swish" and the wheels go round,
Giddy-up, we're homeward bound!

The engine's broken, the engine's broken,
So let's go look for Farmer Dray!
Here comes Dolly, here comes Dolly,
Now we'll soon be on our way, so,

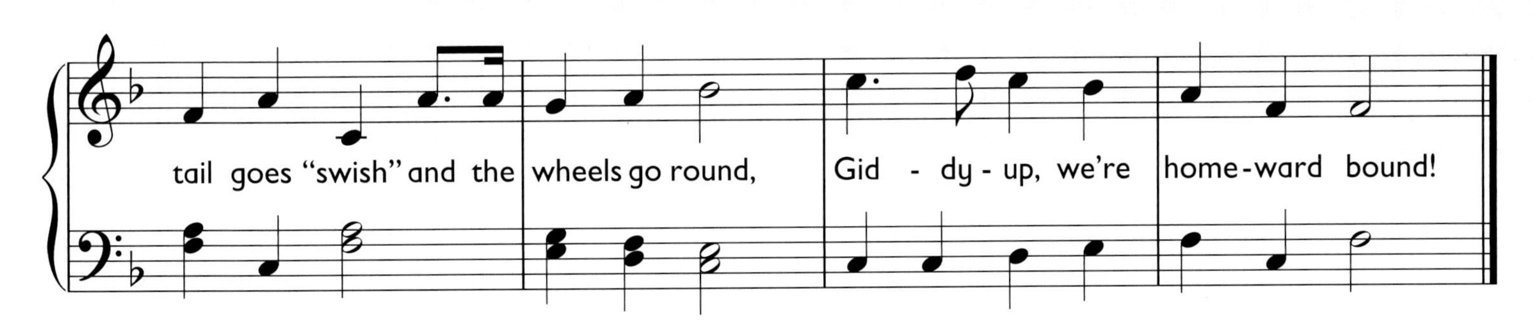

Dolly, Dolly, on your way,
We've got a train to pull today!
Your tail goes "swish" and the wheels go round,
Giddy-up, we're homeward bound!

Pat-a-cake, pat-a-cake

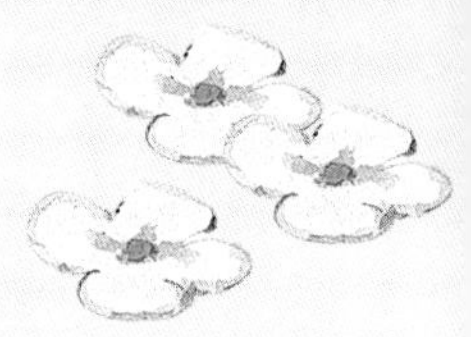

(to the traditional tune)

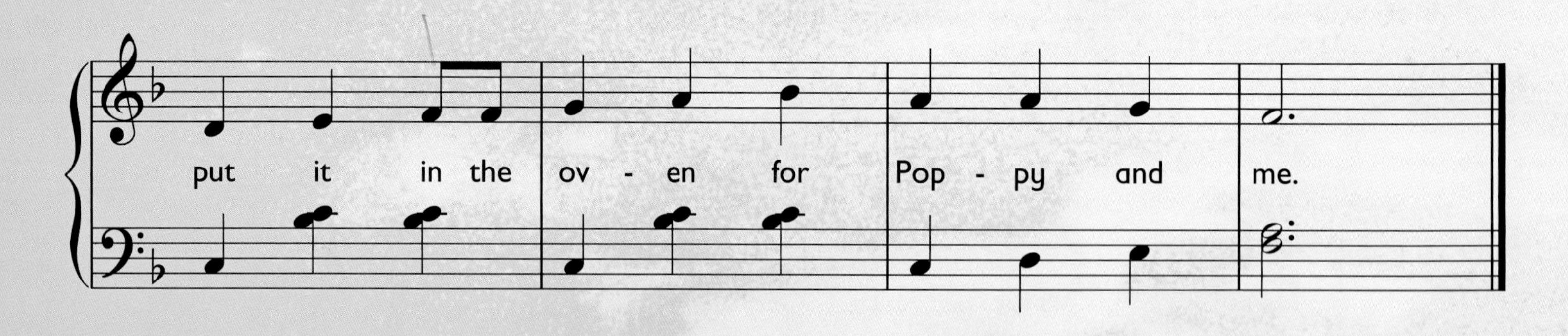

Pat-a-cake, pat-a-cake, baker's man,

(Clap your hands)

Bake me a cake just as fast as you can!

(Rub your hands together)

Pat it and prick it and mark it with "P"

(Use one finger to trace the letter "P" on your palm)

And put it in the oven for Poppy and me.

(Pretend you are eating a cake)

Poppy put the kettle on

(to the tune of "Polly put the kettle on")

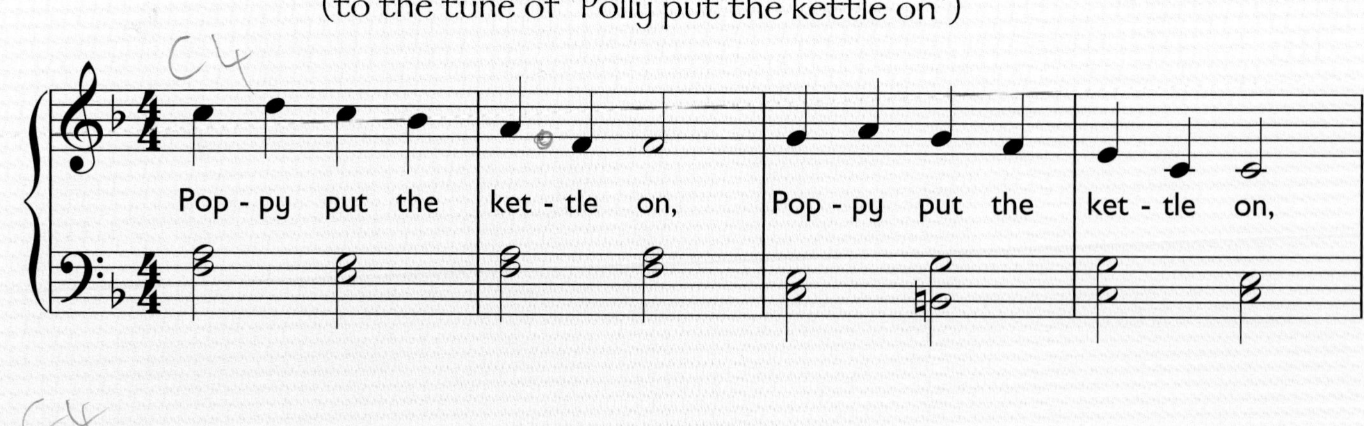

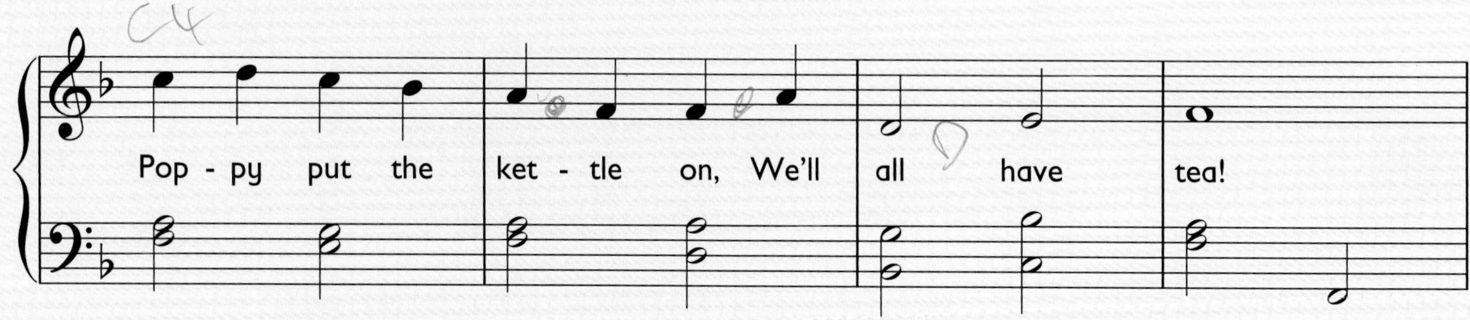

Poppy put the kettle on,
Poppy put the kettle on,
Poppy put the kettle on,
We'll all have tea!

Mrs. Boot has made a cake,
Mrs. Boot has made a cake,
Mrs. Boot has made a cake,
For us to eat.

Scarecrow's secret

(to a new tune)

Scarecrow, scarecrow,
In the field all day,
Scarecrow, scarecrow,
Keep the birds away.

In your bright blue overcoat,
And a scarf around your throat,
Scarecrow, scarecrow,
In the field all day.

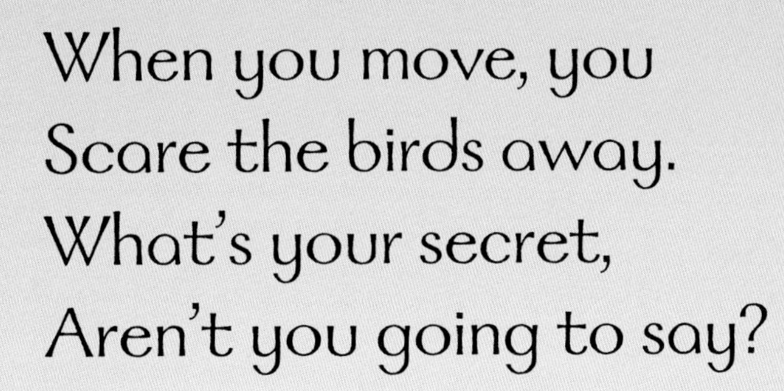

When you move, you
Scare the birds away.
What's your secret,
Aren't you going to say?

Whiskers found a place to hide,
Kept her kittens safe inside,
Scarecrow, scarecrow,
In the field all day.

Twinkle, twinkle, little star

(to the traditional tune)

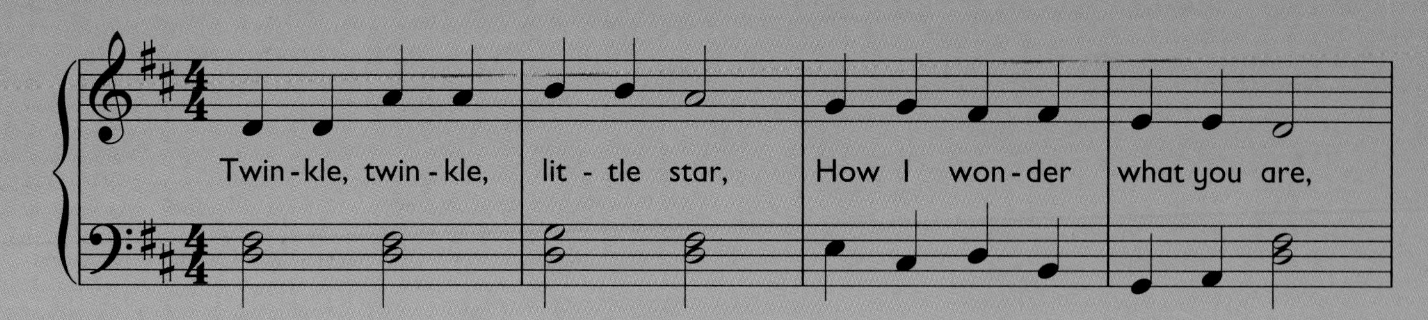

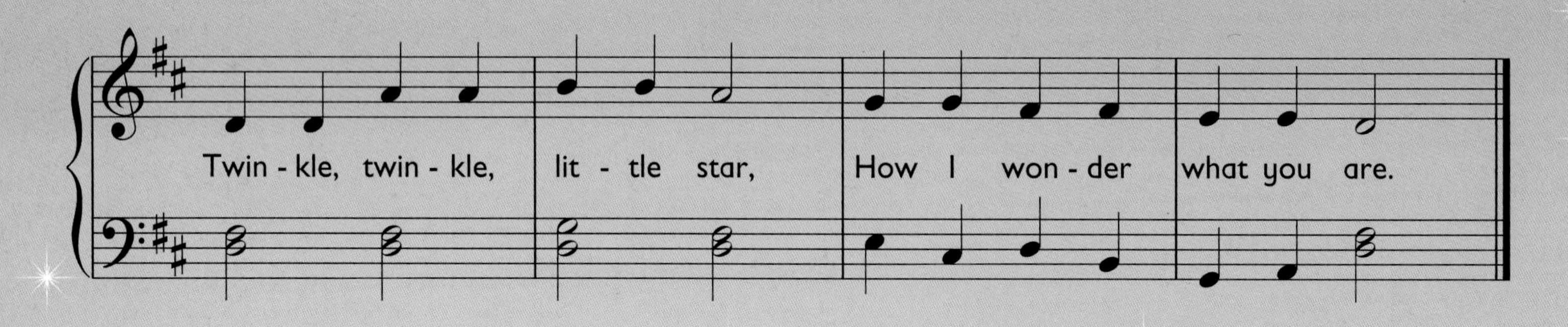

Twinkle, twinkle, little star,
How I wonder what you are,
Up above the world so high,
Like a diamond in the sky,
Twinkle, twinkle, little star,
How I wonder what you are.

When the blazing sun is gone,
When he nothing shines upon,
Then you show your little light,
Twinkle, twinkle, all the night.
Twinkle, twinkle, little star,
How I wonder what you are.

Then the traveller in the dark,
Thanks you for your tiny spark.
Could he see which way to go,
If you did not twinkle so?
Twinkle, twinkle, little star,
How I wonder what you are.

In the dark blue sky you keep,
Often through my curtains peep,
For you never shut your eye,
Till the sun is in the sky.
Twinkle, twinkle, little star,
How I wonder what you are.

One, two, three, four, five!

(to the traditional tune)

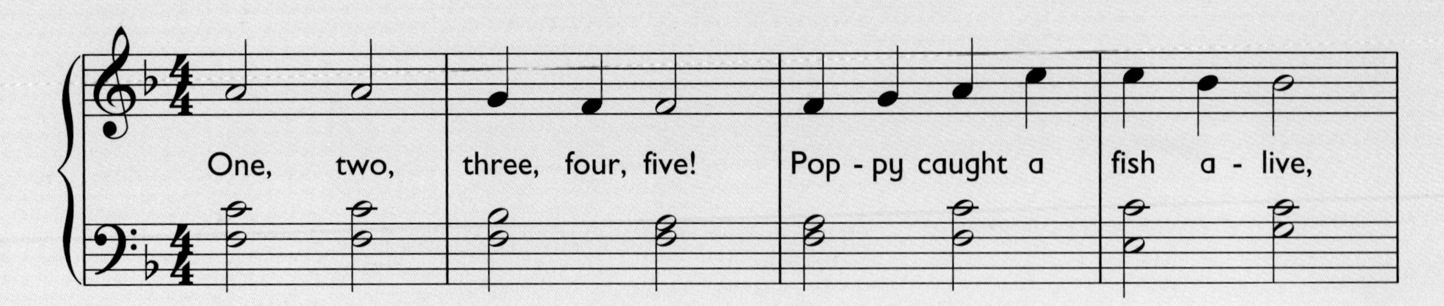

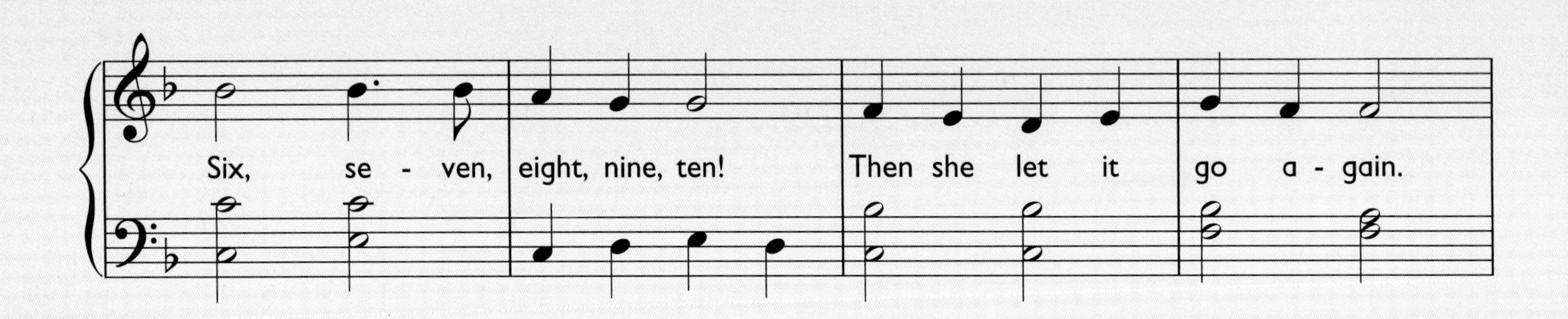

One, two, three, four, five!
Poppy caught a fish alive,
Six, seven, eight, nine, ten!
Then she let it go again.

Why did she let it go?
Because it bit her finger so!
Which finger did it bite?
This little finger on the right!

This little piggy

(to a new tune)

This little piggy went to market,
(Twiddle big toe)

This little piggy stayed at home,
(Twiddle second toe)

This little piggy had roast beef,
(Twiddle middle toe)

This little piggy had none,
(Twiddle fourth toe)

And this little piggy cried
(Twiddle little toe)
"Wee wee wee! I can't find my way home!"
(Tickle sole of foot and up to back of knee)

Woolly had a little lamb

(to the tune of "Mary had a little lamb")

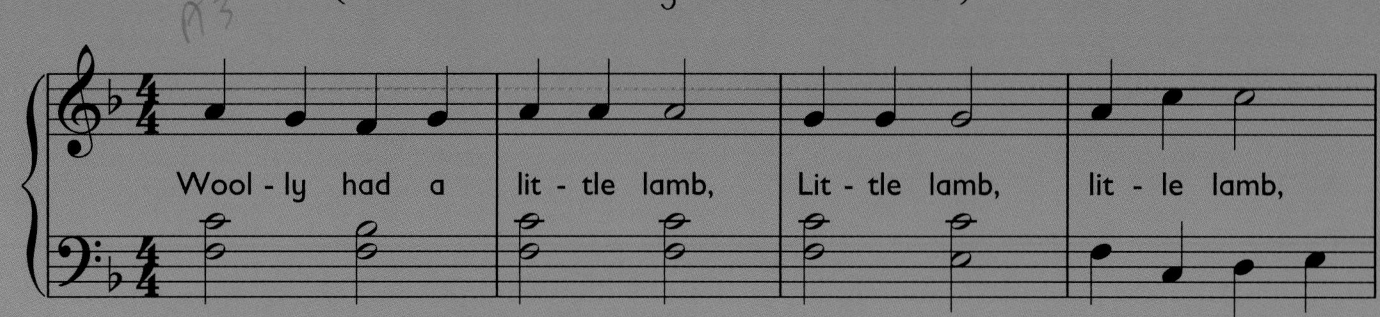

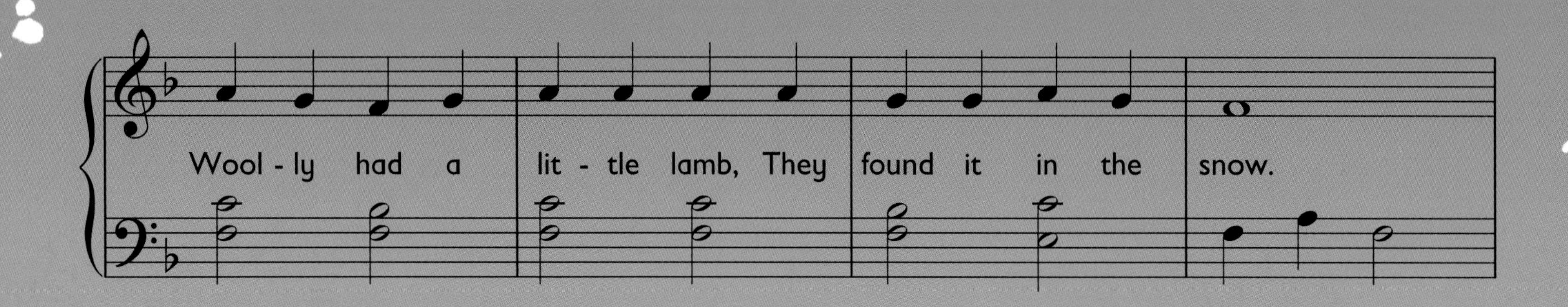

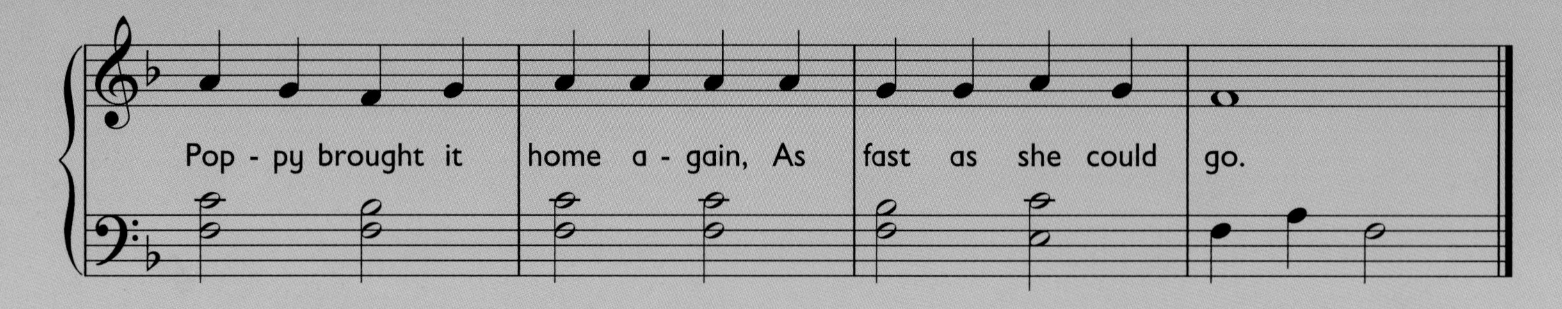

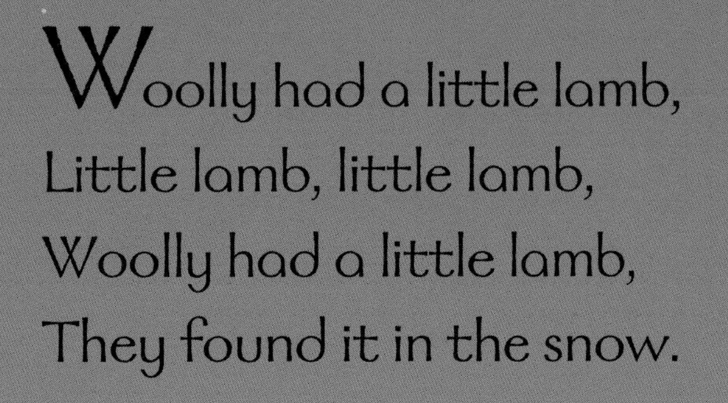

Woolly had a little lamb,
Little lamb, little lamb,
Woolly had a little lamb,
They found it in the snow.

Poppy brought it home again,
Home again, home again,
Poppy brought it home again,
As fast as she could go.

We wish you a merry Christmas

(to the traditional tune)

We wish you a merry Christmas,
We wish you a merry Christmas,
We wish you a merry Christmas,
And a happy new year!

Glad tidings we bring,
To you and your kin,
We wish you a merry Christmas,
And a happy new year!

We all want some figgy pudding,
We all want some figgy pudding,
We all want some figgy pudding,
So bring some out here!

Glad tidings we bring . . .

We won't go until we've got some,
We won't go until we've got some,
We won't go until we've got some,
So bring some out here!

Glad tidings we bring . . .

Tunes in this book

Sam and Poppy had a farm 2
(to the tune of "Old Macdonald had a farm")

Where has our little pig gone? 4
(to the tune of "Where has my little dog gone?")

Hungry donkey 6
(to the tune of "London Bridge is falling down")

Naughty Woolly! 8
(to the tune of "Baa, baa, black sheep")

How many eggs?* 10
(to a new tune)

Sam's little kitten 12
(to the tune of "Pussycat, pussycat")

Dolly, Dolly 14
(to the tune of "Horsey, horsey")

Pat-a-cake, pat-a-cake 16
(to the traditional tune)

Poppy put the kettle on 18
(to the tune of "Polly put the kettle on")

Scarecrow's secret* 20
(to a new tune)

Twinkle, twinkle, little star 22
(to the traditional tune)

One, two, three, four, five! 24
(to the traditional tune)

This little piggy* 26
(to a new tune)

Woolly had a little lamb 28
(to the tune of "Mary had a little lamb")

We wish you a merry Christmas 30
(to the traditional tune)

The songs in this book have been arranged for children's voices and piano. Additionally the top line can be played on a melody instrument such as recorder or violin. (Where there is more than one note in the top line, the melody always follows the upper note.)

Most of the tunes are based on well-known nursery rhymes. Three of them, marked * in the list above, have been specially written for this book. If you have a computer, you can listen to all the tunes to these songs on the Usborne Quicklinks Website to hear how they go. At Usborne Quicklinks you will also find a virtual keyboard that you can use to play simple tunes on your computer. Just go to **www.usborne-quicklinks.com** and enter the keywords "Farmyard Tales Songbook", then follow the simple instructions.

First published in 2005 by Usborne Publishing Ltd, Usborne House, 83-85 Saffron Hill, London EC1N 8RT, England. **www.usborne.com**

First published in America 2005. Printed in Malaysia. UE.